TOP SECRET

UNCOVER YOUR INNER SPY

H. Becker

Scholastic Canada Ltd.
Toronto New York London Auckland Sydney
Mexico City New Delhi Hong Kong Buenos Aires

Scholastic Canada Ltd.
604 King Street West, Toronto, Ontario M5V 1E1, Canada

Scholastic Inc.
557 Broadway, New York, NY 10012, USA

Scholastic Australia Pty Limited
PO Box 579, Gosford, NSW 2250, Australia

Scholastic New Zealand Limited
Private Bag 94407, Botany, Manukau 2163, New Zealand

Scholastic Children's Books
Euston House, 24 Eversholt Street, London NW1 1DB, UK

www.scholastic.ca

Library and Archives Canada Cataloguing in Publication

Becker, Helaine, 1961-, author
Top secret : uncover your inner spy / H. Becker.

ISBN 978-1-4431-4820-7 (paperback)

1. Spies--Juvenile literature. 2. Espionage--Juvenile
literature. I. Title.

UB270.5.B44 2015   j327.12   C2015-906482-1

Cover illustrations: background: Alexis Puentes/Shutterstock, Inc.; sunglasses: onair/ Shutterstock, Inc.; stamp border: CarmenKarin/Shutterstock, Inc.; sonar: Makhnach_S/Shutterstock, Inc.
Interior illustrations © by Shutterstock.com.

6 5 4 3 2 1   Printed in Canada   121   16 17 18 19 20

MIX
Paper from
responsible sources
FSC® C004071
www.fsc.org

Table of Contents

Have You Got What It Takes?

Are you cut out to be a real spy, or are you more suited to a less sneaky career? Answer yes or no to each of the following questions to find out.

1. I am really good at more than one thing — academics, sports, music, the arts. No
2. I'm aces at paying attention. Focus is my middle name. No
3. I blend into a crowd easily. Yes

4. I don't have many secrets — what you see is what you get. No
5. I'm a born leader — or so people tell me. No
6. I am usually the centre of attention. No
7. I am extremely even-tempered. You'll get no drama queen scene from me! Yes
8. I am 100 percent loyal to my friends. But my enemies? Yes
   Hisssssssss . . .
9. I have sky-high self-esteem. No
10. I am a terrific listener. Go on, spill it. Yes

SCORING

1. Yes 25 No 0		5. Yes 0 No 5		8. Yes 15 No 0			
2. Yes 20 No 0		6. Yes 0 No 20		9. Yes 10 No 0			
3. Yes 20 No 0		7. Yes 25 No 0		10. Yes 25 No 0			
4. Yes 10 No 0							

20   50   40

HOW YOU RATE . . .

0-75 Susie Sunshine. Spying takes place in shadowy places, where people lie, cheat and steal. Not your cup of tea, is it? You're too honest, too friendly and just plain too much fun to do the dark dealings espionage requires. Consider a career as a wedding planner or TV broadcaster instead.

76-120 Ms Foreign Correspondent. You love the idea of being a spy, with its foreign travel and glam. But the demands of the spy life don't really suit your share-all nature. A job as an investigative reporter might be the one for you. You get to go to cool places and meet fascinating people. And any dirt you dig up, you can share!

121-150 Sneaky Sally. You are super smart, super athletic and super talented. Yet people hardly ever notice you. That's because your best skill is flying under the radar. Congratulations! You've got the perfect profile for a successful spy.

151+ Double agent. So who are you working for, US or THEM?

Test Your Observation Skills

Spies need to have terrific observation skills in order to suss out their surroundings and recognize signs of danger. Take this quiz to find out if your skills will see you succeed in espionage work.

Take 30 seconds to study the room you are in. Take great care to notice as many details as you can. Turn and face the opposite direction before answering the questions below.

1. How many blue things are there in the room?
2. How many windows are there in the room? Doors?
3. How many round things are there in the room?
4. Are there any edible things visible in the room? List them.
5. Are there any sharp objects (knives, scissors, pens) visible? List them.
6. How many light switches are there?

SCORING

Give yourself 1 point for each question in which you got 1 item correct.

Give yourself 2 points for each question in which you got 2 to 4 items correct.

Give yourself 5 points for each question in which you got 5 or more items correct.

Give yourself 10 points for each question in which you got every item correct (even if there are 5 or fewer of those items in the room).

HOW YOU RATE . . .

0-15 See ya later. You have a promising future in flower arranging. Watch out for thorns.

16-39 Seek your fortune elsewhere. Your observation skills could use some sharpening. Practise this activity often in different rooms and with different items to improve your abilities.

40-59 Seems likely. You have superior observation skills. This ensures you'll see great success as a spy.

60 Sees all. Your observation skills are uncanny. Do you have enhanced robotic vision and recall? Remember, though, to watch your back. Other people have their eyes on you!

Which Fictional Spy Are You?

Are you an evil spy like the cartoon character Natasha, or are you more a regular-kid kind of agent like Harriet the Spy? Answer yes or no to each of the following questions to find out your inner spy personality.

1. If you had a dog, you'd name it Max. *Yea*
2. You like the idea of living in a big city such as New York or Moscow. *No*
3. Admit it: you are secretly afraid of exploding golf balls. *Yea*
4. You are a very picky eater. *No*
5. You ADORE the idea of being a babysitter. *No*
6. You may have wet the bed once or twice in your younger years. *No*
7. Your favourite author is Leo Tolstoy. *No*
8. If you had to choose your fave country, it would be USA over Spain. *No*

9

SCORING

1.	Yes 1	No 0	4.	Yes 4	No 0	7.	Yes 1	No 0
2.	Yes 5	No 0	5.	Yes 0	No 11	8.	Yes 0	No 5
3.	Yes 4	No 0	6.	Yes 10	No 0		

5   11   5

YOU ARE . . .

0-3 Agent 99, from *Get Smart.* You are 100 percent super organized. You love odd people and things, and numbers that are divisible by 11. You could run the world, easy-peasy, if annoying and incompetent (but cute) guys named Max would stay out of your way.

4-7 Natasha, from *The Rocky and Bullwinkle Show.* You love blini, caviar and anyone named Boris, but are deathly afraid of squirrels and moose. You have fabulous hair and are a total diva.

8-15 Harriet the Spy. You like notebooks. You also like writing in notebooks, especially about other people. You are excellent at making up stories and eating tomato sandwiches.

16-20 Kim Possible. You are strong, smart and capable, and wish you already had a high-school diploma. You love cartoons but are not crazy about rodents.

21+ Carmen Cortez, from *Spy Kids.* You are very loyal and family oriented. You have superior computer skills. You are responsible, mature for your age and great at taking care of business.

Which Famous Real-Life Spy Are You?

Fictional spies may be fun, but real-life spies can be even more exciting. Take this quiz to discover which unbelievable-but-true superspy was most like you!

1. Your favourite food is . . .
   a. New-York style pizza.
   b. Canadian bacon.
   c. home-style chicken and fries.
   d. anything exotic!
2. How would you describe yourself?
   a. Determined.
   b. Devious.
   c. Clever.
3. You are . . .
   a. down-to-earth.
   b. an urban sophisticate.
4. Are you good at solving puzzles?
   a. Yes.
   b. Sort of.
   c. No.
5. Which era do you think you'd be happiest living in?
   a. 1700–1799.
   b. 1800–1899.
   c. 1900–1999.

SCORING

1. a1 b2 c10 d12
2. a0 b6 c12
3. a1 b5
4. a15 b5 c0
5. a0 b1 c10

YOU ARE . . .

2-5 355. 355 was the code name for a woman in the Culper Ring, a famous spy network during the American Revolution. Like the real Agent 355, no one knows the real you. You are so mysterious that others are infinitely intrigued by you! Your special gift: counting by fives.

6-20 Laura Secord. Laura Secord risked her life to deliver information about the Americans' strategic plans to the Canadians during the War of 1812. Like Laura, you think no danger is too great if it means protecting those you care about. You like cows and eating chocolate (especially chocolate mousse!). Your favourite item of clothing? Red coats. Your special gift: eavesdropping.

26-29 Harriet Tubman. Harriet Tubman is best known for bringing slaves to freedom on the famed "Underground Railroad." She was also a nurse, cook and spy during the American Civil War. Like Harriet, you are versatile and daring. You love helping people, riding the subway and playing "follow the leader" — especially when you are the leader! Your special gift: playing the tuba.

30-40 Eastern Jewel. Eastern Jewel (Yoshiko Kawashima) was a Manchu princess who was sent to Tokyo as a child. There, she was trained in judo and fencing and became a spy for the Japanese. Like Eastern Jewel, you are physically tough, mentally agile and very precious. Your special gift: throwing things over fences.

41-49 Madame X. Madame X was the code name for Agnes Meyer Driscoll, a code breaker for the Allies during World War I and World War II. Like Madame X, you are smart, subtle and devastatingly effective at every task you do. You love hunting for treasure (X marks the spot!) and alphabetizing. Your special gift: X-ray vision.

50+ Hedy Lamarr. Hedy Lamarr was one of the most popular Hollywood stars during World War II. Both beautiful and brilliant, she invented a method for jamming radio devices so the enemy could not intercept US messages. Like Hedy, you are super smart and terrific at problem solving. You love glamour, glamour and more glamour, but also techy things, such as gaming or coding. Your special gift: using your head.

Are You Cut Out to Be a Sleeper Agent?

Undercover agents are what we think of when we think "spy." Sleeper agents are undercover agents who live in the field under an assumed identity for years. Do you have a future in this risky profession? Take this quiz to find out.

1. You would describe yourself as . . .
   a. patient.
   b. organized.
   c. strategic.
   d. all of the above.
2. Your favourite kind of music is . . .
   a. loud.
   b. whatever other people are listening to.
   c. It depends — sometimes chill, sometimes party tunes.
   d. I don't listen to music.
3. You've changed schools and are the new kid in class. Everyone is looking at you! You . . .
   a. burst into tears.
   b. slink into your seat and hope they eventually lose interest.
   c. smile and say hello.
   d. figure out who are the most popular kids and start hanging with them.

4. You've been given a new assignment: keep a journal and write in it every day. Your teacher promises that what you write is confidential — you will never have to show it to her. You . . .

a. write in it every day.

b. write in it for a while, but then lose interest. By the end of the term, you have only five full pages.

c. decide not to do it. It makes no sense to do an assignment no one will ever read or grade!

d. ask the teacher if she wouldn't mind reading what you write — you'd prefer the feedback!

5. You are working on a class project. You've been assigned to do it in a group. You are . . .

a. annoyed. You prefer to work alone.

b. deliberate. You figure out how to get the best mark by focusing on what each group member does best.

c. excited. You love working in a group.

d. neutral. You do your work, without making waves, no matter what the situation.

6. Which do you enjoy most?

a. Acting or engaging in make-believe play.

b. Playing a team sport.

c. Solving crossword puzzles.

d. Playing an individual sport.

7. People say you are . . .

a. pleasant and easygoing.

b. determined and disciplined.

c. bossy and stubborn.

d. clever and creative.

8. Which is your favourite school subject?

a. Math.

b. Science.

c. Art or drama.

d. Social studies.

HELLO
I AM...
Bossy

9. Which do you prefer?
   a. An adrenalin-rush adventure.
   b. A regular routine.
   c. Keeping things low key.
   d. A little of this, a little of that.
10. You've won a prize for having the best math grade in your class this term. You . . .
   a. frame your certificate of achievement and hang it over your desk.
   b. are thrilled you will get to go up onstage at the award ceremony and be applauded by everyone you know.
   c. don't make a big deal about it — you only tell your closest friends and family.
   d. don't tell anyone at all.

SCORING

1. a1 b1 c1 d5	5. a3 b5 c1 d4	8. a2 b3 c5 d4
2. a1 b5 c2 d3	6. a5 b2 c3 d4	9. a1 b5 c4 d3
3. a1 b2 c3 d4	7. a4 b3 c2 d5	10. a2 b1 c3 d5
4. a5 b2 c1 d3		

HOW YOU RATE . . .

13-20 Under suspicion. You are like a flower — you need sunshine. Hiding out in dark corners, under an assumed identity, is not the best job for you. Perhaps with your superior organizational and social skills, you should consider becoming the Spymaster, in charge of the entire operation.

21-30 Understandably reluctant. You don't like the idea of committing to a long-term assignment. You'd prefer tasks that have clear goals and defined starts and finishes. Perhaps you should consider applying for Special Agent status, so you would only be called in for urgent, but short, assignments. Like overthrowing that evil dictator — or phoning in the Agency's pizza order (no pineapple!).

31-40 Under appreciated. You excel at keeping a low profile. You are just sneaky enough, and persistent enough, to make a terrific sleeper agent. Take plenty of naps to prepare for your assignment!

41-49 Under where? You've mastered all the skills needed to bring down the enemy — they'll get caught with their pants down, but you'll be nowhere in sight.

Do You Know Your Spy Slang?

Would you rather be a birdwatcher or a carnivore? Or would you enjoy being a musician? And what would you do if you found yourself in "hospital"? Get the skinny on a spy's secret lingo and find out how well you understand Sneak Speak.

1. A birdwatcher is . . .
   a. a camera.
   b. a spy.
   c. a hotel window.
2. What's Camp Swampy?
   a. The United States' training base.
   b. A code name for a surveillance operation.
   c. A meeting place.
3. Carnivore is . . .
   a. an FBI computer program.
   b. a Russian assassin.
   c. a spy who talks too much and must be pulled from the field.
4. What's a hospital?
   a. German slang for the United States.
   b. American slang for the Kremlin, the seat of Russian government.
   c. Russian slang for prison.
5. Which spy penetrates enemy spy organizations?
   a. A mole.
   b. A vole.
   c. A ghoul.
6. What is a musician?
   a. A person who fakes, or "fiddles" documents.
   b. A radio operator.
   c. A target who "sings" and provides valuable information.

7. Should you worry if you've been "blown"?
   a. No, because it means you've been given a new identity and sent out to the field.
   b. Yes, because it means you've been captured.
   c. Yes, because it means your cover has been compromised.
8. Pocket litter is . . .
   a. items that are placed in a spy's pocket, such as receipts or coins, that make her assumed identity seem more authentic.
   b. an inflatable dummy used to allow a live agent to escape unseen.
   c. useless information gathered during a failed mission.
9. Uncle is . . .
   a. a Spymaster.
   b. spy headquarters.
   c. a coded call for help.
10. What's a bug?
    a. A spy who has defected to the other side.
    b. A secret message.
    c. A listening device.

SCORING

Give yourself one point for each correct answer.

1. b	5. a	8. a
2. a	6. b	9. b
3. a	7. c	10. c
4. c		

HOW YOU RATE . . .

0-3 Slang starting gate. You've got your foot in the spy-slang door! Now please remove it.

4-7 Slang slinger! You can use spy slang effectively — to order a sandwich in the caf at spy headquarters.

8-9 Slangtastic! Your spy slang is top-notch!

10 Slanguage expert! You've written the spy-slang dictionary!

Spy World

Can you match the spy agencies listed here with the countries they work for?

1. CSIS
2. MI6
3. RAW
4. CIA
5. KGB
6. DGSE
7. ASIO
8. Fiji Intelligence Services
9. MSS
10. Mossad
11. PSIA
12. GRU

a. India
b. France
c. Australia
d. Canada
e. Former Soviet Union
f. Russia
g. Japan
h. China
i. Fiji
j. Israel
k. United Kingdom
l. USA

SCORING

Give yourself one point for each correct answer.

1.	d	5.	e	9.	h
2.	k	6.	b	10.	j
3.	a	7.	c	11.	g
4.	l	8.	i	12.	f

HOW YOU RATE . . .

0-3 Country retreat. Best avoid foreign travel for now.

4-6 Country of origin. You are starting to know the players on the spy-world stage.

7-8 Country music. You're getting into the rhythm of the spy biz!

9-12 Country club. You may apply for membership in the spy elite!

Honest or Sneaky?

Take this spy-eye glimpse into your secret nature and find out what it reveals about your spyworthiness.

1. You observe someone cheating on a test. You . . .
   a. tell a friend, in confidence, about what you saw.
   b. tell the teacher.
   c. tell no one.
   d. tell the cheater you saw them cheat.

2. You forgot to empty the cat's litter box, like you'd promised. Now your mom — and Fluffy! — are annoyed. What do you do?

   a. Whine that it's not fair you always have to do the stinky jobs, then stomp off in a huff.
   b. Make up a crazy excuse: "I was going to do it but then I was spirited away by aliens! They only just released me!"
   c. Avoid your mom — and Fluffy — until someone else changes the litter.
   d. Apologize and promise to do better next time.

3. You find a $50 bill lying on the floor right outside your school's staff room. You . . .
   a. ask a few friends if they know who it belongs to, then keep it if no one knows.
   b. keep the money and tell your friends you got it as a present.
   c. go into the staff room and ask who dropped the cash.
   d. keep the money and don't tell anyone about it.

4. Your dad asks you if you think his golf swing is improving. You . . .
   a. tell him you have no idea, and that's the truth.
   b. tell him it looks great, even if it isn't true.
   c. tell him the truth, even if it hurts his feelings.
   d. make a joke and avoid answering.

5. A kid you don't like much asks you to come over after school and hang out. What do you say?
   a. "Sure!" But then disappear as soon as the school bell rings.
   b. "Maybe another time. I have other plans today."
   c. "Sure!" Then go and suffer.
   d. "No, I don't think so. Sorry."

6. You are playing a game of HORSE with a friend. It's your turn, and your shot misses — you have lost the game! But your friend has lost track of how many times you've missed and thinks you have one more chance left. What do you do?
   a. Nothing. Maybe she is the better scorekeeper and you lost track.
   b. Nothing. Tough luck if she lost count.
   c. Tell her that she's mistaken and congratulate her on winning.
   d. Ask her, "Are you sure? Because I thought that was my E shot."

7. Your parents told you, "no screens for a week!" But by Tuesday, your mom has forgotten about the rule. What do you do?
   a. Keep those screens off. You know the rules.
   b. Turn on the game console and play *Spyville* all afternoon.
   c. Go hang with your friends where you can use *their* screens without your mom knowing, but come home early because you feel guilty.
   d. Remind your mom and hope she'll let you off the hook since you were honest about it.

8. You accidentally spilled grape juice all over your friend's lunch bag. Nobody saw you do it. You . . .
    a. tell your friend that you saw someone else spill the milk on it.
    b. keep quiet and hope she doesn't ask you about it.
    c. tell your friend you did it, but then give a long explanation for why it wasn't your fault.
    d. confess ASAP and promise to pay for a new lunch bag.

SCORING

1. a2 b1 c3 d4	4. a1 b2 c4 d3	7. a1 b4 c3 d2
2. a2 b4 c3 d1	5. a2 b4 c3 d1	8. a4 b3 c2 d1
3. a2 b4 c1 d3	6. a3 b4 c1 d2	

HOW YOU RATE . . .

8-10 The truth teller. You can't help it — you don't like lying. Besides, everybody can see right through you when you do, so there is no point! As a result, people can trust you — and that makes you a good candidate for espionage work.

11-17 The slider. You prefer to be honest but hate facing consequences. So if you can convince someone to cover for you, or make up an excuse that will keep you out of trouble, that's the choice you tend to pick. Spymasters find this quality challenging in an agent; can they trust you when the chips are down?

18-28 The avoider. You hate conflict and try to avoid hurting someone's feelings, making a decision or being forthright about your own

opinions. You aren't always sure about what's the *right* thing to do, so you often pay more attention to what's the *safest* thing to do. A spy needs a strong moral compass. Figure out who you are and what you believe in — then stick to it — if you want to have a career in espionage.

29-32 The sneak. You have a clear sense of right and wrong. It just doesn't matter much to you. What matters more is how you can take advantage of any situation and make it work for you! While this sneaky strategy can be very useful in a spy, it will also mean your Spymasters will keep you on a very, *very* short leash. You're supposed to be working for them, after all, not yourself.

What Is Your Secret Spy Identity?

Your life as an ordinary kid is a great cover story, or legend. Living how you do, people won't discover your true identity as a spy. But *we* know who you are. Take this quiz to reveal your secret spy identity.

1. You prefer . . .
   a. running and jumping. > Go to question 3.
   b. singing and dancing. > Go to question 2.
2. You love . . .
   a. unusual animals, such as llamas. > Go to question 4.
   b. visiting unusual places, such as lamaseries. > Go to question 5.
3. You like to imagine your future as . . .
   a. filled with glitz and glam. > Go to question 8.
   b. rustic and relaxing. > Go to question 9.
4. Your favourite food is . . .
   a. cheese. > You are BRIE CAMEMBERT.
   b. fish sticks. > You are TINA TUNAFISH.
   c. chicken. > Go to question 8.
5. You prefer . . .
   a. being the centre of attention. > Go to question 6.
   b. observing from the sidelines. > Go to question 7.
6. You prefer . . .
   a. singing. > You are HIP HOP HANNAH.
   b. horseback riding. > You are CALAMITY JADE.
7. You prefer . . .
   a. having people do things for you. > You are PRINCESS ALEXA.
   b. doing things for others. > You are PATTY CAKE.

8. You prefer games that are . . .
   a. fast and full of action. > Go to question 10.
   b. require strategy. > Go to question 11.
9. You prefer . . .
   a. doing things on your own. > Go to question 13.
   b. group activities. > Go to question 14.
10. Which sport do you prefer?
    a. Hockey. > You are KATY WICKENHEIMER.
    b. Basketball. > You are CARMEN THE KNIFE THROWER.
    c. Sailing. > You are ROSE FORTUNE.
11. Money or power?
    a. Money. > You are ARLENE CHICKENSON.
    b. Power. > Go to question 12.
12. Which city would you prefer to live in?
    a. Ottawa. > You are AMBASSADOR MOO.
    b. Hollywood. > You are RINGABELLA
       MOANER.
13. You prefer . . .
    a. nature. > You are THE GIRL NEXT DOOR.
    b. technology. > You are THE BOY NEXT DOOR.
14. Which game would you rather play?
    a. Hide-and-seek. > You are THUMBELINA SLIRK.
    b. Fetch. > You are I. M. ABEAGLE.

YOU ARE . . .

Ambassador Moo. You were plucked from an embassy of a foreign nation, one that enjoys chewing cud and swatting flies. Your mission: to find and disable a listening device disguised as a cow patty.

Arlene Chickenson. HQ found you in math class, where you were already such a whiz with numbers that you had established fourteen successful businesses and racked up a gazillion-dollar portfolio before your eighth birthday. Undercover, you use your head for numbers to find and secure enemy operatives' filthy lucre. (You sure like to make a *buck, buck, buck!*)

Brie Camembert. You were discovered working in your family's cheese factory. Your mission: to identify who is the real Big Cheese in Limburgerville, enemy HQ. With your unparalleled ability to smell a rat (and make the world's best grilled-cheese sandwich), your photo will soon grace the Wall of Heroes at HQ. (Don't forget to say cheese when they snap the photo!)

Calamity Jade. You used to compete in rodeos. Now you use your extreme gymnastic skills and ability to shout "Yee-haw!" at the top of your lungs to lasso enemy agents into submission. Remember: You can lead a horse to water, but you can't make him drink the truth serum. And quit yelling "Yee-haw!" during science class!

Carmen the Knife Thrower. HQ found you performing awesome feats of derring-do in a circus in Spain. You can slice a chicken into eighths from forty paces — we don't even want to say what you could do to an unprepared enemy. Let's just say she will wind up with a very unusual haircut.

Hip Hop Hannah. Because of your talent for rhyme and fancy footwork, you were getting noticed — by the wrong people (those slimy, rhymy enemies!). HQ saved you and is now training you in secret to decode enemy messages hidden in musical numbers performed at talent shows around the world.

I. M. Abeagle. HQ found you at an agility-dog event, where you were training your champion poodle, Puff, to jump through hoops and race up and down teeter-totters. You find it very difficult to maintain your cover as an ordinary kid because you really, really loved being top dog. You love giving commands and hate being told what to do! What makes this gig possible, though, is that you are loyal to a fault.

Katy Wickenheimer. In "real" life, you are a hockey goddess. Your slapshot is a thing of beauty, and your breakaway? Breathtaking. When your case officer calls, you will use your secret icy skills to score a hat-trick — identify, neutralize, dispose — on your enemy. SCORE!

Patty Cake. You used to love to bake — cakes, cookies, you name it. You use your kitchen skills in new ways now that you're undercover, like cooking up new surveillance methods (edible cameras!) and convincing targets to talk (they'll confess all for just one bite of your irresistible snickerdoodles!). Your friends would be amazed by what you can do with a rolling pin (*YOW!*) or lemon zester (*EEK!*).

Princess Alexa. Your grandmamma, Princess Anastoogia, survived the Shushin Revolution and escaped by the skin of her teeth. Your family has lived in hiding ever since. Now your spy cover as a regular kid saves you from assassination attempts by your royal family's enemies *and* gives you an excellent opportunity to spy on George Stinkoff, the architect of your family's misfortune and a truly evil creep.

Ringabella Moaner. You were on your way to becoming a child star when HQ approached you. Why use your incredible charisma for fame and fortune, they asked, when instead you can use your unique acting gifts to pretend to be ordinary? You agreed, because you truly believe keeping the planet safe from evil is more worthwhile than getting an Oscar. And having a mansion in Hollywood. And adoring fans . . . Wait! STOP! Ringabella, where are you going?

Rose Fortune. You are an excellent sailor, and your skills on the high seas are noted on your dossier as "FULL SPEED AHEAD." Your favourite expression is "anchors away," and your mission of choice would be sneaking up on the enemy in a submarine.

The Boy Next Door. Who would ever suspect you in your current feminine disguise? Sure, you've had to learn how to wear a skirt without showing your undies, and how to squeal at the top of your lungs when you are happy. But so what? You enjoy pretending to be a girl, because girls rock!

The Girl Next Door. You are mild mannered and polite. On the surface, that is. But beneath your serene exterior, you have always craved excitement and thrive when the stakes are high. Your cover story is close to your real-life identity, making every minute of your life a thrill-ride, since discovery may be but a heartbeat away.

Thumbelina Slirk. You used to be the kind of person who could hide in plain sight — the one no one ever called on in class, even when you raised your hand so high your knuckles scraped the ceiling. When you approached Spy Central for a job, they made you wait for six hours in their torture chamber of a waiting room (it smelled like feet!). But now, your extreme patience and talent for invisibility (and ability to endure foul odours) is an asset. What was your name again?

Tina Tunafish. You are very slippery — even your Spymasters have a hard time pinning you down! You love water sports, tin cans and music — especially pentatonic scales. You became a spy because you always felt like a fish out of water in school. Now you are a fish out of water in spy HQ.

What's Your Spy IQ?

The history of espionage is rich and fascinating. How well do you know your craft's storied past? Take this quiz to test your knowledge of spy facts from yesterday and today.

1. Barbara Lauwers ran a spy ring made up of German prisoners of war that infiltrated villages and spread anti-Hitler propaganda during World War II. What was it called?
   a. Operation Ker-P.O.W.
   b. Operation Sauerkraut.
   c. Operation Barbie.
   d. Boo Hitler Club.
2. What is the name of Canada's spy agency?
   a. CSIS.
   b. MI5.
   c. NSA.
   d. Canadarm.
3. During the American Civil War, spy Emeline Pigott hid secret messages . . .
   a. in her elaborate hairdo.
   b. in her baby's diaper.
   c. in a dish of macaroni salad.
   d. in the folds of her hoop skirt.
4. Virginia Hall was a spy for the Allies during World War II. She had a wooden leg. What was Virginia's nickname?
   a. Ginger Snap.
   b. Claudette Normand.
   c. The Limping Lady.
   d. Peggy.

5. One of the spies most feared — and most wanted — by the Nazis was called "The White Mouse." Her real name was Nancy Wake. She . . .

   a. killed an enemy agent with a single karate chop to the throat.

   b. hid secret messages in blocks of Limburger cheese.

   c. worked as a courier for the French Resistance.

   d. both a and c.

6. British spies on assignment in Moscow once hid secret messages inside . . .

   a. fake rocks in a local park.

   b. sausages for sale in a local market stall.

   c. the Kremlin's washrooms.

   d. fake toenail clippings.

7. Three of the four following famous actresses were spies for the Allies during World War II. Which one was *not* a spy?

   a. Hedy Lamarr, an Austrian-born Hollywood star.

   b. Marlene Dietrich, a German-born Hollywood star.

   c. Greta Garbo, a Swedish-born Hollywood star.

   d. Judy Garland, an American-born Hollywood star.

8. Who was the real James Bond?

   a. A double agent named Agnes Smedley.

   b. An ornithologist and the author of a reference book called *Birds of the West Indies.*

   c. A famous French chef.

   d. A Canadian real estate agent.

9. The phrase "flaps and seals" is spy lingo for . . .
   a. a swimming pool.
   b. a code breaker.
   c. the art of opening envelopes and parcels undetected.
   d. a signed confession.

10. During the American Civil War, Sarah Emma Edmonds disguised herself as a man named Frank Thompson and spied for the Union Army. Sarah was born in . . .
    a. Nova Scotia.
    b. New Brunswick.
    c. Quebec.
    d. Ontario.

SCORING

Give yourself one point for each correct answer.

1. b	5. d	8. b
2. a	6. a	9. c
3. d	7. d	10. b
4. c		

YOUR SPY-SCHOOL REPORT CARD . . .

0-3 B. New to school.

4-6 B+. B-coming better every day.

7-8 A-. Almost excellent!

9-10 A+. A is for awesome!

☑ AWESOME!
☐ Excellent
☐ Very Good
☐ Satisfactory
☐ Marginal

Spy Versus Spy

Is the spy trivia presented here the real deal, or is it counter-intelligence provided to trick you? Answer true or false to each question.

1. The infamous Agent Fifi, who was tasked with making sure Britain's spies were reliable, was a poodle.
2. Women often excel at spycraft because men tend to underestimate their abilities.
3. A famous French chef was actually an American female spy who created a recipe for a shark repellent called Shark Chaser, to keep sharks away from underwater explosives.
4. During World War II, British spies used special shoes that left behind footprints that appeared to be made by bare feet.
5. During the American Civil War, Union spy Elizabeth Van Lew sent secret messages in hollowed-out eggs.
6. The Canadian spy agency, CSIS, did not allow women to work for them until 1985.
7. A spy known as the Doll Lady (because she owned a fancy doll shop) didn't receive her university degree until 19 years after graduation because she hadn't returned some books to the library.
8. Spies for Queen Elizabeth I paid Shakespeare to write a coded message into the text of *Romeo and Juliet*. Unwitting actors delivered the message to a Spanish double agent in the play's audience and thereby saved England from the Spanish Armada.
9. Invisible ink can be made using urine.
10. During World War II, the Germans sent a spy to Canada. He liked his new country so much, he refused to spy. Instead, he turned himself in!

SCORING

Give yourself one point for each correct answer.

1.	F	5.	T	8.	F
2.	T	6.	F	9.	T
3.	T	7.	T	10.	T
4.	T				

HOW YOU RATE . . .

0-3 All trick, no treat. You've been duped by the enemy!

4-6 Card trick. You've got an ace up your sleeve when it comes to sniffing out trickery.

7-8 Magic trick. You have special powers that protect you from being duped.

9-10 Hat trick! No one can fool you!

36

Under Pressure

Do you crack under pressure, or are you calm, cool and collected in any situation? Find out how you rate against other potential spy recruits when it comes to nerve-racking assignments.

1. You have to take a super-ginormous standardized test. There will be 100+ people in the room — and no windows! You . . .
   a. feel your heart pounding in your chest and your palms start to sweat, but you remind yourself it's just a test, like all the others you've taken before. You take a deep breath, flip your paper over and answer the questions.
   b. go blank.
   c. know you've got this in the bag. You listen to the teacher's instructions, answer the questions and hand in your paper before everyone else.

2. You are at bat. Bottom of the ninth. The score is tied, but if you hit a home run, your team will score the winning run. You . . .
   a. keep your eye on the pitcher and wait for the perfect pitch.
   b. swing at the first pitch.
   c. step out of the batter's box three, four times to calm down. Then hope and pray you don't miss the ball completely.

3. Your sister accuses you of losing her favourite sweater. You didn't do it. You . . .
   a. offer to help her look for it.
   b. feel your lip start to tremble and your eyes fill with tears as you explain you had nothing to do with it.
   c. stomp out of the room in a huff. How dare she accuse you!

4. A boy you sort of like comes up to talk to you. You . . .
   a. talk to him normally. He's a normal person, after all, even if he is a boy.
   b. freeze like a deer in headlights.
   c. ramble on like a fool and hope he doesn't notice your cheeks have turned flamingo pink.

5. Which situation would you find the most unnerving?
   a. Suddenly waking up and finding yourself as the new kid in a new school.
   b. Skateboarding through a tough course that you've never tried, in front of a crowd.
   c. Grounded for an entire week — no screens!

6. You accidentally betrayed a friend's confidence. You plan on fessing up in the morning. You . . .
   a. toss and turn all night, fretting about it.
   b. feel better now that you've made up your mind to tell her.
   c. fake a stomach ache in the morning so you don't have to face her.

7. You are at your Granny Tillie's 90th birthday party. Aunt Esmerelda has asked you to carry the tea things into the living room. You don't even want to imagine what will happen if you drop Granny Tillie's priceless teacups! You . . .
   a. can handle it. You take the tray, sashay into the living room and say, "Tea, anyone?"
   b. stammer, "I have to go to the washroom!" and run for it.
   c. reluctantly take the tray. Your hands shake and the tea sloshes as you shuffle across the room. Although you make it to your destination safely, it takes you a solid half hour before your heart rate returns to normal.

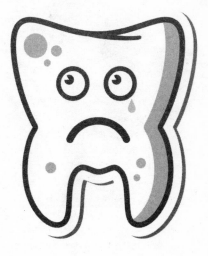

8. You're at the amusement park with five of your closest friends. You stop to tie your shoe. When you stand back up, everyone is gone! You try to text your pals, but there's no signal. You're on your own, in the middle of Panicland! You . . .

   a. immediately take off for the Dragoncoaster ride. It's at the other end of the park, but you're pretty sure that's where they'd be heading. Or maybe it was the Haunted House . . .

   b. sit down on the closest bench and wait for your friends to come back and find you — that's the plan you agreed to if you got separated.

   c. burst into tears, run to the nearest ride operator and announce in a quavery voice, "I'm lost!"

9. You're at the beach when you notice a fin in the water! You . . .

   a. laugh — it looks just like a shark! Then go back to what you were doing.

   b. scream, point and urge everyone out of the water!

   c. watch it for a few minutes. You'll see what it really is before you act.

10. Your tooth is really loose and hurts like crazy! You . . .

    a. beg your dad to let you stay home from school — it hurts too much to think!

    b. find it super annoying, so you yank it out yourself.

    c. spend the day wiggling it, wiggling it, wiggling it, and worry about how much it might bleed when it falls out.

SCORING

1. a3 b1 c5	5. a5 b3 c1	8. a3 b5 c1
2. a3 b2 c1	6. a2 b5 c1	9. a2 b1 c5
3. a3 b2 c1	7. a5 b1 c3	10. a1 b4 c3
4. a3 b1 c2		

HOW YOU RATE . . .

10-20 Pressure cooked. You're cool as a cucumber, if you mean a cucumber that has been boiled in a soup. With hot sauce.

21-35 Pressure sensitive. You can take the heat — as long as it's room temperature.

36-43 Impressive! You're hot stuff when it comes to keeping your cool under pressure!

Peacock or Chameleon?

Spies frequently need to blend in with the woodwork to achieve their missions. Find out if you have the sneaky skill of hiding in plain sight.

Answer true or false to each question.

1. I listen more than I talk.
2. I talk with my hands.
3. People often confide in me.
4. I tend to speak loudly and with conviction.
5. When I'm in a conversation, my voice and body language often change to mirror the other person's.
6. I enjoy talking about myself and entertaining others with stories.
7. People don't know the real me.
8. I am easily flustered.
9. I consider myself a very private person.
10. I am very energetic, and have trouble sitting still.
11. I have sometimes told a little white lie to get along with others.
12. I am not a people pleaser.
13. I think most people can be manipulated to believe what you want them to believe.
14. Others find it easy to manipulate me.
15. I have excellent observation skills.
16. I am charismatic — people seem to be drawn to me and want to hang out with me.
17. I enjoy my own company.
18. I am very emotional.
19. I have simple tastes in food.
20. I love dressing fashionably.

41

SCORING

Add up your TRUE answers for all the ODD-numbered questions.

_____5_____

Add up your FALSE answers for all of the EVEN-numbered questions.

_____

Add the two totals together for your score. _____

HOW YOU RATE . . .

0-3 Peacock. People can't help but notice you! You have that mysterious something called "star quality." Forget a career as a field agent — unless your cover is a Hollywood Box Office Phenom.

4-9 Zebra. You are bold in how you present yourself, but you don't share everything with everybody — you are very selective in both who you trust and what you reveal. You are surprisingly good at camouflaging your secrets — even you don't always realize it!

10-16 Teddy bear. You prefer it when everybody around you gets along, so you try not to make waves by stating your opinions or feelings too forcefully. As a result, people find you easy to hang out with and are likely to confide in you. An excellent skill set for gathering intelligence!

17-20 Chameleon. You are skilled at hiding your true feelings and opinions. When you don't want to be noticed, you can make yourself completely invisible. That can be very useful for a spy. But remember: being able to speak up and speak out are important skills too. You'll have to tell HQ what you discovered eventually, right?

Memory Challenge

Do you have a terrific memory? Spies need to have a good eye for detail and an even better memory. Some of the questions below ask about information that appears earlier in this book. But don't be tempted to look for the answer before answering the question, or you'll automatically fail the test.

1. Was there a woman in the notorious Culper Ring?
   a. Yes.
   b. No.
2. What animal is pictured on page 18?
   a. A rat.
   b. A mole.
   c. A vole.
3. What was the real name of the spy known as the Limping Lady?
4. Which of these three pictures does NOT appear anywhere else in this book?

   a.   b.   c.

5. Which fictional spy character is NOT named in this book?
   a. Cody Banks.
   b. Agent 99.
   c. Carmen Cortez.
6. The Table of Contents lists how many quizzes?
   a. 25
   b. 28
   c. 30

7. On page 5 there is a crowd scene. Which unusual item is shown in the picture?
   a. A bird flying upside down.
   b. A toaster.
   c. A cloud shaped like a turnip.

8. In which quiz does the word "swampy" appear?
   a. Under Pressure.
   b. Do You Know Your Spy Slang?
   c. Spy Versus Spy.

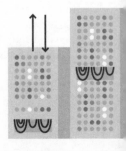

9. Do you remember your score for the SECOND quiz you took in this book?
   a. Yes
   b. No

10. Do you remember the first question in this quiz? What was it?

SCORING

Give yourself one point for each correct answer below.

1. a	5. a	9. a
2. b	6. b	10. Do you have a terrific memory?
3. Virginia Hall	7. a	
4. b	8. b	

HOW YOU RATE . . .

0-3 Forget it. Your mind is like a steel trap — without the steel. Or the trap.

4-7 Memory maestro. You have excellent recall. Or you're a top-notch liar. Either way, don't forget to apply for spy school — you'll be a star recruit!

8-10 Five billion gigabytes of RAM. You have a mind like a supercomputer — what goes in, stays in. Until you need it, that is. That's when you display flash-drive-fast recall and 110% accuracy. Skip the program description — go straight to the top of the spy school class!

Can You Decode Parentspeak?

Being a spy means being able to understand what people are saying, even when they are speaking in code. Parents are notorious code talkers. Match the Parentspeak code phrases on the left with what the adults are really saying on the right.

1. You're going to be late for school!
2. Did you wash behind your ears?
3. I'll think about it.
4. You're a wonderful kid!!!
5. There's something I'd like talk to you about.
6. It's going to be fun!
7. Have you thought this through?
8. I think you need some quiet time.
9. It's a new recipe. What do you think?
10. Do you want to talk about it?
11. I don't like your attitude.
12. Sit up straight.
13. Did you do your homework?
14. Can we talk about this later?

a. I sure hope you did your homework!
b. It is not going to be fun.
c. That might not be such a good idea...
d. I don't like when you disagree with me.
e. I definitely need some quiet time.
f. You're a wonderful kid!
g. I have some bad news.
h. WARNING! Weird ingredients ahead!
i. You smell a little funky...
j. I'm really, really, *really* tired.
k. You look like an amoeba right now.
l. You have at *least* five more minutes before you have to get going.
m. No!
n. I love you and am concerned about you.

SCORING

Give yourself 1 point for each correct answer.

1. l	5. g	9. h	12. k
2. i	6. b	10. n	13. a
3. m	7. c	11. d	14. j
4. f	8. e		

HOW YOU RATE . . .

0-4 Novice decoder. Do you often find yourself confused when speaking with your folks? That's partly because parents don't only communicate verbally — they often rely on body language. Pay attention to what their eyes, faces and posture reveal, not just the words they say, to better develop your Parentspeak decoding skills.

5-8 Level II decoder. You've got the basics down. Before long you will understand members of the opposite sex, too.

9-12 Advanced placement. You have an excellent grasp of Parentspeak. You are now ready to learn Teacherspeak.

13-14 Super decoder. Go to the head of the class. There is nothing left to teach you.

Kooky Spook Quiz

1. What do you call an underwater spy?
   a. Glub.
   b. James Pond.
   c. Dr. S. Cuba.
2. What kind of shoes do spies wear?
   a. Sneakers.
   b. Shhhhhoes.
   c. Stilettos.

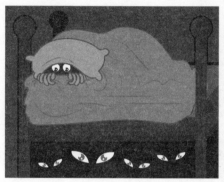

3. Why did the spy stay in bed?
   a. She was embedded in an enemy agency.
   b. She was a sleeper agent.
   c. She was working undercover.
4. Why hire a frog as a spy?
   a. They are great at croak and dagger missions.
   b. They are good at disguise — they are all actually princes!
   c. They are slimy.
5. Why did the duck become a spy?
   a. She was actually a swan undercover.
   b. She was down on her luck.
   c. She was good at quacking codes.
6. What spy do you often enjoy at Christmastime?
   a. Meat pie.
   b. Mince pie.
   c. Pumpkin pie.
7. Which part of a horse is best at espionage?
   a. Its mane
   b. Its tail.
   c. Its hide.

8. Why do doctors make great spies?
   a. Because they frequently perform operations.
   b. Because they are good at treating bugs.
   c. Because they have lots of patients.
9. How do spies make contact with their spy ring?
   a. They call them on cell phones.
   b. They meet at the designated jewellery store.
   c. They play "Twinkle Twinkle Little Star" on handbells.
10. What do spies-in-training receive at spy school?
   a. Permission slips.
   b. Plenty of Cs (Sees).
   c. Extra-spicy recess snacks.

SCORING

Give yourself a point for each correct answer. Add them up to get your results.

1.	b	4.	a	7.	c	9.	a
2.	a	5.	c	8.	a	10.	b
3.	c	6.	b				

HOW YOU RATE . . .

0-3 Funny gal! Your spy skills are a real joke.

4-6 Sly spy. You can pick locks with that sharp wit!

7-8 Hilari-espionage. You are the Spymaster of silliness.

9-10 Legendary. You are the queen of counter-intelligence and terrible puns.

Break the Code (Easy)

A substitution code is one of the earliest codes ever used. To create one, letters of the alphabet are replaced with new letters using a simple pattern; for example, you shift each letter of the alphabet by six positions, as shown below:

A B C D E F G H I J K L M N O P Q R S T U V W X Y Z
(original alphabet)

G H I J K L M N O P Q R S T U V W X Y Z A B C D E F
(new alphabet)

When you write a coded message, you substitute a letter from the new shifted alphabet for the original one. A becomes G, G becomes M, R becomes X, etc.

So the word CAT, coded, would be spelled IGZ.

To decode the message, simply match the letters from the new alphabet to the original alphabet: IGZ becomes CAT.

See if you can decode the following secret messages using this substitution code.

1. YVEQOJY XUIQ!

2. MXKGZ PUH LOMAXOTM
   UAZ ZNOY IUJK!

3. IUJKY IGT HK G RUZ UL LAT CNKT EUA
   YNGXK ZNKS COZN EUAX HLLY.

4. O YVE COZN SE ROZZRK KEK...

5. ZNKXK OY G ZCU-CGE SOXXUX OT ZNOY
   HUUQ. IGT EUA LOTJ OZ?

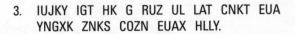

49

SCORING

Give yourself one point for each correct answer.

1. Spykids rock!
2. Great job figuring out this code!
3. Codes can be a lot of fun when you share them with your BFFs.
4. I spy with my little eye . . .
5. There is a two-way mirror in this book. Can you find it?

HOW YOU RATE . . .

0-1 GIK! You're off to a great start as a code breaker.

2-3 YAVKX! Before you know it, you'll be dreaming in code.

4 IUJK HXKGQKX! The Secret Message Department of CSIS will be calling you.

5 USM! Time to invent your own codes — you are too clever for us.

Break the Code
(A Little Harder)

A trickier kind of substitution code uses keywords to shift the letters of the alphabet. For example, if the keyword is SPYKID, the shifted alphabet would look like this:

A B C D E F G H I J K L M N O P Q R S T U V W X Y Z
(original alphabet)

S P Y K I D A B C D E F G H I J K L M N O P Q R S T
(new alphabet)

In this keyed code, A becomes S, but Y also becomes S (this is what makes this code doubly tricky — some letters can have two possible matches!)

So the word CAT, coded, would be spelled YSN.

To decode the message, simply match the letters from the new alphabet to the matching original alphabet: YSN becomes CAT or CYT; can you figure out which of the two is right? Of course you can!

See if you can decode the following secret messages using this keyword substitution code.

1. GIIN GI SN NBI PONYBIL MBIJ.

2. QSNYB OIL GI SN NBI YFIYE MBIJ.

3. NBCM FIHIFS MJS CM GCMMCIH SIO.

4. NBCM PIIE CM FCMNIHCHA...

5. ...PIYSOMI CN CM QILECHA OHKILYIPIL!

51

SCORING

Give yourself one point for each correct answer.
1. Meet me at the butcher shop.
2. Watch for me at the clock shop.
3. This lonely spy is mission you.
4. This book is listening . . .
5. . . . because it is working undercover!

HOW YOU RATE . . .

0-1 ALISZ! You're on your way! (If only you knew where you were going!)

2-3 NSFIHNIK! Now if only you could remember your locker combination.

4 YIHALSNM! You've got MECFFM as a code breaker!

5 MOJILMJS! You're BCLIK!

52

Break the Code (Even Harder)

Breaking a **code** is easy when you know the **basic** principle and the keyword. But what if you don't? In this code, there are *five separate keywords* hidden *in this paragraph.* Identify them, code breaker! Then use each one to create a new **shifted** alphabet just like you used in **the** previous coded quiz. You will need to

use all five shifted alphabets to **decode** the enemy's secret correspondence, below. Each shifted alphabet will decode just one of the five sentences. You must decide which alphabet goes with which sentence.

UKQ CNA OAEJC SCPDDAE!!!

TJPM CICHT DN OCC SGCQCMCNO JA NKTFDIN.

HNKG SEE MAT FHINFTGML.

THTKALK QEB JFPPFLK.

LOH EIL SIOL FCED!

SCORING

Give yourself one point for each sentence you were able to decode:

1. Keyword: CODE. Message reads, "You are being watched!!!"
2. Keyword: BASIC. Message reads, "Your enemy is the cleverest of spykids."
3. Keyword: SHIFTED. Message reads, "Burn all the documents."
4. Keyword: THE. Message reads, "Abandon the mission."
5. Keyword: DECODE. Message reads, "Run for your life!"

HOW YOU RATE . . .

1 Level 1 Code breaker. Your next task: untangling the chain on a necklace.

2-3 Level 5 Code breaker. Your next task: finding a needle in a haystack.

4 Level 20 Code breaker. Your next task: putting Humpty Dumpty back together again.

5 Level 100 Code breaker (highest level ever!). Your next task: achieving world peace.

Break the Code (Toughest)

Substitution codes are tough, but when you look at them, you *know* you are looking at a coded message. More challenging secret messages don't even *look* like secret messages. Steganography is the art of hiding messages within non-secret text. Check out the school assignment below. There is a secret message embedded in it for you. Can you find it and read it?

NAME: _____   DATE: _____

ANIMAL MYSTERY
Find the names of thirteen mammals hidden
in this word jumble!

D	E	A	R	A	T	R	A	G	W
S	E	N	A	T	Y	O	P	U	A
L	R	M	B	I	S	R	I	S	L
O	O	I	B	O	N	A	G	A	R
T	S	T	I	S	I	C	G	N	U
H	C	A	T	M	H	C	E	N	S
T	I	S	M	E	M	O	O	S	E
T	O	D	O	G	R	O	R	D	O
W	E	L	L	L	I	N	N	S	S
C	R	A	E	B	H	O	O	L	E

SCORING

Give yourself 1 point for each mammal you found. Give yourself 10 points for each word in the secret message that you found. Give yourself 100 bonus points if you figured out the complete secret message!

Bear	Moose	Rat
Cat	Otter	Raccoon
Dog	Pig	Sloth
Horse	Rabbit	Walrus
Mole		

The secret message says:
Dear Agent, your mission assignment is to do well in school!

HOW YOU RATE . . .

0-13 Level 5 Code breaker. You have a future as a zookeeper.

14-100 Level 10 Code breaker. You have a future as a word jumble puzzle writer!

101-219 Level 20 Code breaker. You have a future as a computer technician in the code department at spy HQ.

220+ Top Level Code breaker. Your job as a chief cryptologist is waiting for you!

Mission Impossible?

Imagining a situation in your head, and determining what you would or wouldn't do in advance, can be a great way to practise your spy skills safely. This quiz has been designed to simulate a typical day at spy middle school. Answer the questions to find out if you would survive or if you'd get sent back to spy kindergarten.

1. A small notebook has appeared inside your school locker. When no one is looking you . . .
   a. put it into your backpack. > Go to question 2.
   b. read it. > Go to question 3.

2. Back in class, you hear a ticking sound. You . . .
   a. get the notebook from your backpack and read it. > Go to question 3.
   b. realize the notebook is actually a bomb in disguise and yell, "FIRE!" > Go to question 4.
   c. wonder who has the really loud and annoying wristwatch. > Go to question 5.

3. The notebook is written in a mysterious code that looks like a recipe for plum pudding. You . . .
   a. hurry home after school to start making plum pudding for dinner. > Go to question 6.
   b. get out your special decoding pen and try to crack the message. > Go to question 7.

4. You and your classmates race out the door. Sigh — it's pouring rain. While you are standing in the playground, getting drenched, you notice there is an eerie light emanating from the principal's office, AND your BFF has slipped away from the crowd and is now running from the playground! You . . .

a. decide that you should read the notebook — ASAP! > Go to question 10.

b. decide to chase after your BFF — ASAP! > Go to question 11.

5. At lunch, you hear the ticking sound again. You realize it is coming from the walls of the building itself. You get a squiggly feeling in your stomach. When the recess bell rings, You . . .

a. casually say to your BFF, "Let's go outside now." > Go to question 8.

b. get out the mysterious notebook and read it. > Go to question 10.

6. You begin pulling out ingredients to make the plum pudding and discover secret messages — several mysterious phrases written on each of them. Together, they read, "There is an enemy spy embedded in your school. All we know is that the spy has black hair and a moustache. Identify, observe, but do not confront — the enemy operative is extremely dangerous." You can think of only one person at your school with black hair and a moustache — the teacher-librarian, Mr. Gouache! The next day, you . . .

a. pretend to return a book to the library. Instead, you use the time to spy on Mr. Gouache. > Go to question 12.

b. remember that rehearsal for the school play is scheduled for lunchtime. You sneak in and see your BFF has gotten the lead role as Burt Backtrack. She is wearing a black wig and moustache! > Go to question 13.

7. You . . .

a. succeed at cracking the code. The message reads, "There is an enemy spy embedded in your school." > Go to question 18.

b. find the code is too hard to solve between classes, so you resolve to work on it after school. > Go to question 19.

8. Outside, you tell your BFF about the strange sound. She says she heard it, too. Then she tells you she found a mysterious notebook in her locker. She pulls it out of her backpack and it looks exactly like yours! You . . .
   a. take yours out and show it to her. She says, "That's weird. I got the same book! What do you think it says?" > Go to question 9.
   b. say, "So you are the enemy agent I was supposed to find and neutralize! HQ told me you would have been given a notebook that looks like this one!" She points it at you and — *ka-boinnnng!* — distracts you by shooting you on the left earlobe with a rubber band that flies from its spine. > Go to question 16.
9. You sit down together and discover both notebooks are written in code. Each book provides the clue to decode the other. You have to work together to decode both notebooks. They say . . .
   a. The girl with the crooked canine tooth (your BFF) is really fun. She came up with this great game. Aren't you glad I'm your BFF? > FRIENDSHIP FUN-MISSION ACCOMPLISHED.
   b. The girl with the crooked canine tooth (your BFF) is your contact. Give her the microchip that is hidden in your shoelace tip. Then go play four square. > MISSION ACCOMPLISHED.
   c. The girl with the crooked canine tooth (your BFF) has betrayed you. Neutralize her! > Go to question 17.
10. The notebook says, "Principal Dugood is an enemy spy. Do not let her fool you into leaving the building. If you do, she will set off the green goo device and destroy the world! You . . .
    a. burst into tears as green goo rains down upon you, turning you and all your classmates into a neon-green liquid food replacement. > MISSION FAIL.

b. race back into the school and corner Principal Dugood just as she is about to press the big green button. You subdue her, fasten her hands behind her back with your special spy-issue (extra strong and won't slide!) hair elastic and destroy the greening device with a swift karate kick to the button. > MISSION ACCOMPLISHED, but you will be demoted to mopping the washroom at HQ until further notice for failing to look at the notebook in a timely manner.

11. You sprint after your BFF, tackle her and . . .
   a. accuse her of being an enemy spy on a terrorist mission to blow up the school. She laughs and says, "You're right! You're not the only spy here! But look, the school is gonna blow in 5 . . . 4 . . . 3 . . ." > Go to question 14.
   b. ask her politely where she is going. She says, "I realized I got some weird green goo on my hands, so I thought I'd go home for a minute and wash them, then come back." > Go to question 15.

12. You observe . . . nothing of interest. You report back to HQ, and they are not impressed. They want proof! You return the next day and the next, but still nothing. You . . .
   a. decide to confront Mr. Gouache directly. He is indeed the enemy spy and is both bigger and stronger than you, so he is able to lock you in the supply cupboard until his backup arrives to whisk you away to a dark, dank cell in a secret prison somewhere near Gimli, Manitoba. > MISSION FAIL.
   b. continue to report what you see to HQ. While you cannot always guarantee you will find out the information you are sent to get, you can behave in a professional spy manner. Giving up, or trying something on the fly that is not in your brief? Those would be mission fails. But sticking with a frustrating mission requires superb spy skills. Nice job. > MISSION ACCOMPLISHED.

13. You share your observations with HQ. The next day, during math class, your BFF is called to the principal's office. Through the classroom window, you see her being forced into a black car by three women in black suits! You . . .

    a. congratulate yourself. > MISSION ACCOMPLISHED.

    b. feel sad, and consider trying to rescue her. But then you think better of it. She always cheated at HANGMAN anyway. > MISSION ACCOMPLISHED.

    c. decide you made a terrible mistake and decide to rescue her. You leap through the window, pulling out your doggifier gun as you go. But she is quicker. She shoots you and your colleagues with her doggifier gun. You all are transformed into cute canines, and while you stare in astonishment at your fuzzy little paws, she escapes. > MISSION (WOOF!) FAIL.

14. You hold her down with one foot so she cannot flee as you fish inside your backpack for the "notebook." It is actually a remote-control bomb-disabling device. You defuse the bomb, wait for backup to arrive and hand over the enemy spy for further questioning. > MISSION ACCOMPLISHED, but now you have no one to eat lunch with.

15. You believe her. She is your BFF, after all, and she's always had a thing about clean hands. You help her up, just as you hear a loud *KABOOM!* The school has exploded! Your BFF pulls out a clown gun and turns it on you. "You were pretty fun to play four square with, but now it's time to move on. Bye, Bozo!!" She shoots you with the clown gun, you instantly grow a mass of rainbow hair and a red nose, and while you stare in shock at your brand-new giant clown feet, she escapes! > MISSION FAIL.

16. You . . .
    a. gasp in astonishment. The rubber band bounces off your left earlobe. It's no ordinary rubber band, though; it's a horrifying new weapon HQ had warned you about — an X32-FREEZE enemy ice-cubifier band! You soon feel your body turning to ice. > MISSION FAIL.
    b. hold up your own notebook, which acts as a deflecting shield so the rubber band (which is actually an enemy-issued weapon called an X32-FREEZE enemy ice-cubifier band) bounces off. You say, "My mission was to unmask the enemy spy by inventing a story about a strange ticking sound. You went along with it so I knew right away you were the spy. Oh, and by the way, your ice-cubifier band just landed on your pinky toe, so you will become frozen in place until my backup comes to arrest — and defrost — you." > MISSION ACCOMPLISHED.
17. You . . .
    a. neutralize her by putting her to sleep with a long, boring story about rodents. > MISSION ACCOMPLISHED.
    b. you laugh — this is too funny! Who made these clever and hilarious books anyway, your sis? *WHOMP*! Your former BFF and current enemy operative hits you over the head with one of the notebooks. She knocks you out cold. > MISSION FAIL.

18. You make a list of possibilities: Candy Kane, the girl who always gives you the stinkeye; Ms Whipple, the grade 6 teacher who always gives out too much homework; the girl named Natasha Imaspyski who recently moved to your city from Plusha, a totalitarian regime on the other side of the world. You observe them all, making careful notes for weeks. Thanks to your meticulous observations, you . . .

a. identify the spy as Natasha Imaspyski. > MISSION ACCOMPLISHED!

b. completely fail to notice your BFF has been scribbling weird notes in a small black book and talking to three women in dark sunglasses and black suits every day after school. Whoops! She is the enemy agent! > MISSION FAIL.

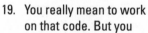

19. You really mean to work on that code. But you have swimming lessons, then homework, and your mom insists you clean up your room before bed. You forget. When you wake up in the morning, you learn that your city has been invaded by Kookrainians and you are now living in a police state. If only the secret agent in place had received the secret intelligence that could have stopped the invasion! You realize with a sinking feeling that *you* had received the intelligence, but it is still sitting at the bottom of your backpack. You sigh and start memorizing the Kookrainian national anthem. > MISSION FAIL.

Spy Logic Puzzle Test

Being able to think on your feet is
job one for Agent 001 — a.k.a. you.
In the field, you will be required to
solve tricky problems on your own,
using nothing but — *gasp!* — your
own logical-thinking skills. These
problem-solving questions were
taken directly from ICU Academy's
entrance exam. Can you figure out
the answers and win your place at
the academy?

1. Add one letter to make a word:
   ENY
2. What is the fourth word that would complete this set?
   big, small, black, white
3. Complete this sentence: Red is to green as _____ is to blue.
4. What eight-letter word has the letters K, S and T in the middle, in
   the beginning, and at the end, but has only one each of the letters
   K, S and T?
5. Which word does NOT belong in this set?
   kumquat
   pomelo
   rhubarb
   mangosteen
   cherry
6. Each word in the proverb below is scrambled. The order of words
   is scrambled, too. What is the proverb?
   SAMEK AWSTE THASE
7. How much is 5 + 5 + 5 x 5 x 5 x 5 x 5 x 0?

8. Each word in this ladder is only one letter off from the words above and below it. Fill in the missing words to correctly complete the ladder.

CORN

CORE

_____

DONE

_____

FINE

9. This grid contains the names of girls that belong to a secret spy ring. Identify them by spelling their names using letters that are connected horizontally, vertically or diagonally, like the one highlighted: LUCY. There are more than 12 girls' names in this grid! How many can you find?

M	I	E	N	A
E	L	Y	L	I
N	M	A	U	Y
Y	N	M	R	C

10. Which is heavier, ten kilograms of feathers or ten kilograms of steel?

SCORING

Give yourself 1 point for each correct answer, except for number 9.

1. D (deny) or V (envy)
2. White.
3. Orange.
4. Inkstand. (The word "in" is at the beginning, the word "and" is at the end, and KST are in the middle!)
5. Rhubarb. The rhubarb we eat is made up of stems from the rhubarb plant. All the rest are fruit — the part of the plant that contains seeds.
6. Haste makes waste.
7. 0.
8. CONE, DINE.
9. Give yourself 1 point for each of these names you found: Amelie, Ann, Anne, Elena, Emily, Emma, Layla, Lena, Lucy, Mary, May, Mila. Did you find any other names? Congrats, but those folks are not members of the spy ring.
10. Neither. They both weigh ten kilograms.

HOW YOU RATE . . .

0-4 Thank you for your application. You are on the waiting list for entry to the spy academy.

5-11 Success! You have been admitted to spy kindergarten.

12-19 A+. You have been awarded a scholarship for entry to Antarctic spy school — bring your long johns and mittens for your advanced program in espionage and waddling like a penguin.

20+ Go to the head of the class. You will be teaching it, after all.

Spot the Spy

Each of the pictures on the next few pages shows a snapshot of a place. Can you spot the spy in each picture?

1.

2.

3.

4.

6.

5.

ICU Academy Mid-term Exam — Advanced Logic Problems

These problem-solving questions were taken directly from ICU Academy's mid-term exam. Can you figure out the answers and keep your place at the academy?

1. Dr. Schnitzel's twin brother has died! But the man who died didn't have a brother. How is this possible?

2. If 3 secret agents can "neutralize" 3 enemy spies in 3 minutes, how long will it take 100 Secret Agents to "neutralize" 100 enemy spies?

3. The following coded message contains the names of three places you must visit for your mission. What are they?

   New pig in! In rage. Nice red fort.

4. What kind of room has no doors or windows?

5. I am a kind of tree that you carry in your hand. What am I?

6. What mathematical symbol can be placed between 5 and 9, to get a number greater than 5 and smaller than 9?

7. You have received the following coded message from HQ:

$$
\begin{array}{r}
S\ E\ N\ D \\
+\ M\ O\ R\ E \\
\hline
M\ O\ N\ E\ y
\end{array}
$$

In reality, the message contains a sequence of numbers needed to unlock a safe at enemy HQ. Each letter represents a single number between 0 and 9. Find the numbers that make the math equation true, and you will also find the code for the safe.

8. There are three light switches in the boardroom at enemy HQ. Each switch turns on or off one of three incandescent light bulbs in the room directly above. Your mission: identify which switch turns on each light bulb. You can move all of the switches to any position as many times as you like, or leave them as long as you like, but you can only go upstairs once to see which lights are on or off. How will you complete the mission successfully?

9. You are an astronaut in a one-person spacecraft. An important part of your mission is to monitor fuel consumption. At liftoff, you have 15,057 litres of fuel in the reserve tank. One minute into the launch, the booster rockets turn on. This uses up 4,781 litres of fuel. Five minutes into the flight, the booster rockets are jettisoned. That takes an additional 2,238 litres of fuel. In addition, the spacecraft uses 560 litres of fuel every minute.

   At the fifteen minute mark, ground control will call the spacecraft to find out how much fuel remains. They will ask the crew to identify themselves. What will the crew say in reply?

10. Each of the animals below can be found in the name of at least one other animal. What are they?

    CAT
    GOOSE
    ANT
    BAT
    EMU
    LION

SCORING

Give yourself one point for each correct answer.

1. Dr. Schnitzel is a woman. She and the dead man are fraternal twins.
2. 3 minutes.
3. Winnipeg, Regina, Fredericton.
4. A mushroom.
5. A palm tree.
6. A decimal point: 5.9 is greater than 5 and smaller than 9.
7. $9,567 + 1,085 = 10,652$
8. Move one light switch to the on position. Leave it as it is for several minutes. Then turn it off, and turn a second switch on. Go upstairs. One lightbulb will be lit; it corresponds to the switch you currently have turned on. Touch the other two bulbs. The one you had previously turned on will feel warm; that bulb corresponds to the first switch you turned on. The third bulb will correspond to the third switch, the one that you had not yet turned on.
9. You are the crew, so you will reply by telling them your name!
10. Caterpillar, mongoose, anteater, antelope, wombat, lemur, stallion

HOW YOU RATE . . .

0-2 BASE camp. You get to stay at ICU Academy for the next term!

3-5 Trail ride. You get a Certificate of Achievement! (It will self-destruct immediately.)

6-8 On the ascent. You skip a grade at ICU Academy!

9-10 Top of the mountain. You've got the highest test score ever recorded! Take over teaching grade 5!

Mission 2 — What Would You Do?

This quiz is designed to simulate a typical mission. Answer the questions to find out how well you might do at real-life espionage in the field.

1. You have been sent undercover to Montreal, where you will be attending circus school with a famous circus troupe. You choose as your act . . .

   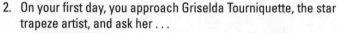

   a. trapeze artist. > Go to question 2.

   b. equestrian artist, doing gymnastics on horseback. > Go to question 3.

2. On your first day, you approach Griselda Tourniquette, the star trapeze artist, and ask her . . .

   a. "Are you an enemy agent from the Republic of Ripoff?" > Go to question 4.

   b. "Do you have a spare pair of tights? I ripped mine." > Go to question 5.

3. Your horse is unaccountably afraid of you and shies whenever you approach her. You . . .

   a. speak softly in horsespeak (neigh!) to her. > Go to question 17.

   b. decide you will ask for another assignment — as a lion tamer. > Go to question 18.

4. Griselda laughs and says, "Of course!" You . . .

   a. now know she is your key contact — your code words match. You go to a nearby café to discuss your next move. > Go to question 6.

   b. now know she really is the incredibly arrogant enemy agent you were sent to neutralize: Miss Cannottellalie. > Go to question 7.

5. Griselda looks at you suspiciously but hands you the tights. Later you analyze the fibres for mysterious substances and discover they bear traces of obnoxia, a toxin that makes people avoid you. Now you must decide how it got there. You think . . .
   a. Griselda was doused with obnoxia by an enemy agent. > Go to question 10.
   b. Griselda accidentally got obnoxia on her tights when she was mixing a batch. > Go to question 11.
6. At the café, Griselda tells you that the circus school's ringmaster, Monique Tweak, is a double agent from the Republic of Rathnelly. She has befriended several politicians in the highest levels of government. You . . .
   a. agree to return to the circus school and tape a sign that reads "kick me" to her back. > Go to question 8.
   b. agree to feed her misinformation to derail her efforts to learn government secrets. > Go to question 9.

7. You have to figure out what Griselda is up to before your big circus-school performance in just three hours. You . . .
   a. fool her into coming to your dressing room, where you tie her up with trapeze wire and threaten to talk to her in a creepy robot voice until she confesses. She says, "Anything but the robot voice!" and tells all. > MISSION ACCOMPLISHED.
   b. tell her there is a rip in her skirt and offer to fix it for her. While you "fix" it, you accidentally on purpose poke her with the safety pin, which has been prepped with your own patented truth serum. As you fix the rip, she tells you everything you could possibly want to know — about stamp collecting. She isn't the enemy agent after all! > MISSION FAIL.

8. You craft a special jacket out of wormskin and sequins that, under bright lights, reveals the words "KICK ME." You . . .

a. give it to Monique, who wears it to the next public performance. Everyone laughs. She dashes out of the ring and disappears into the night, never to be seen again. > MISSION ACCOMPLISHED.

b. hide it in Monique's dressing room. When she spots it, she decides it must belong to the lion tamer, Ima Hunter. Ima puts it on for her act; the lion kicks her (not hard). And while the crowd laughs at the audacious routine, you send photos of Monique to HQ. Her cover blown, she disappears into the night, never to be seen again. > MISSION ACCOMPLISHED.

9. You drop hints to Monique that your mom is a serious bigwig in Government Procurement and is responsible for buying 100 trillion dollars' worth of new tanks, which will be delivered that very evening to your house during the circus performance! Monique acts like she isn't interested. You try to draw her out by . . .

a. showily unfolding a map that reveals the location of your house with the words "TANK DELIVERY HERE" on it. Her lip twitches. You believe she has taken the bait! > Go to question 15.

b. offering to help her with her makeup for the performance. > Go to question 16.

10. You decide Griselda is the intended target. Now you must determine who else in your circus-school troupe might be the agent — and why they were targeting Griselda. You immediately become suspicious of . . .

a. Unita Banana, because she is supposed to feed the elephants but she is always whispering into the collar of her costume. > Go to question 12.

b. Larissa Chang, because you have seen her fiddling with the wires on the trapeze Griselda will use for her big finale. > Go to question 13.

75

11. You now believe Griselda is a brilliant
and talented enemy spy, but a little
bit on the messy side. You decide to
bring her a treat: a chicken parmigiana
sandwich loaded with mushrooms,
onions and red sauce. You . . .

a. hand her the sandwich and watch
as, just like you predicted, she spills
the red sauce on her costume.
With her outfit ruined, Griselda
quits the circus. But now she wants revenge — against
YOU! > MISSION ACCOMPLISHED, but you have made a very
dangerous, if sloppy, enemy.

b. unwrap the sandwich under her nose but don't let her touch
it, because the special "sauce" emits a chemical that reacts
with the traces of obnoxia on her outfit. And if it drops on
the outfit, it will explode on contact! When they combine in
the air, however, a noxious smell arises that makes everyone
(except you!) flee the premises. You grab Griselda and hold
her fast. > Go to question 14.

12. When Unita is in the washroom, you
"accidentally" knock her costume
from the peg in the dressing room.
When you pick it up, you discover
there is a microphone hidden in the
collar! And when you tap it, you hear
a voice speaking to you in Rath-
nelese! You . . .

a. immediately contact HQ and report
the identity of the spy. > MISSION
ACCOMPLISHED.

b. yell into the mic, "I smell a
Rathnelly!" Then barricade Unita
in the washroom until backup — who turns out to be Griselda!
— arrives. > MISSION ACCOMPLISHED.

76

13. You tell Griselda to delay her finale until you flash her a signal with your shining white teeth. In the meantime, you shadow Larissa. You catch her packing her things in the elephant's trunk — he's a thief too! — and discover a one-way ticket back to Smink in the pocket of her sparkly skirt. You tie her up with agency-issued duct tape repair Griselda's frayed trapeze wire (also with duct tape), and flash Griselda the signal — the show must go on, after all! > MISSION ACCOMPLISHED.

14. With Griselda under your control, you decide to . . .
    a. send her to a dank, dark prison somewhere near Gimli, Manitoba, where she will live out the rest of her life. > MISSION ACCOMPLISHED.
    b. turn her into a double agent, working as a mole inside her government to spy on them for you! > MISSION ACCOMPLISHED, and you get a super-huge promotion and a lifetime supply of trapeze tights.

15. You tell HQ to expect Monique to appear at 12 Snee Key Drive at 8:30. Then you put on your outfit and prepare for your stellar debut as a trapeze artist. > MISSION ACCOMPLISHED.

16. Since you don't trust her, you offer Monique your very special lipstick. It makes her lips swell up so badly she has to go to the hospital, where your colleagues, disguised as doctors, take her medical history. Through clownishly swollen lips, she inadvertently reveals many of her own government secrets! > MISSION ACCOMPLISHED.

17. The horse still won't cooperate with you. She tries to stamp on your foot and gets horse snot on your costume. A juggler named Fantasia Tickle comes to your rescue by offering you a sugar cube to feed her. You . . .
    a. take the sugar cube and feed it to the horse. > Go to question 19.
    b. say, "Thanks, but sugar is bad for horsey teeth. I will build her trust using my sweet voice and uncommon horse sense." > Go to question 20.

18. It turns out that when you were a child living in Leonia, you befriended a lion cub who had a thorn in its paw. That was the very same lion who is now working for the circus! You perform flawlessly together, winning the trust and admiration of all who see you. Everyone in the circus wants to be your friend. You live happily ever after with your friendly lion and huge circle of circus pals. > MISSION FAIL, but who cares? You are having so much fun!

19. The horse eats the sugar cube and hiccups. That makes both you and Fantasia laugh. Before long, you and Fantasia are fast friends, and not just because you are riding around the ring on a very fast horse while she juggles flaming torches from the back of a running bear. But you can't help noticing she spends a lot of time tying her shoes. You decide . . .

    a. to ignore it — she probably just has very slippery laces! > Go to question 21.

    b. to investigate further — she could be sending coded messages using shoelace signals. > Go to question 22.

20. Fantasia rolls her eyes at you and says, "Silly girl! Don't you know Whinny is an enemy agent? She won't ever trust you, and if you are smart, you won't trust her either!" Is Fantasia telling the truth? You decide to take a closer look at Whinny. You start at . . .

    a. the rear end. You detect a strange smell coming from her horsey heinie. > Go to question 24.

    b. the front end. You hear a strange sound coming from her horsey head. > Go to question 25.

21. You were right — her laces ARE slippery. But ignoring that fact was a terrible mistake, because so is she! Fantasia is a slippery, sneaky spy! But she's become your best friend. What will you do?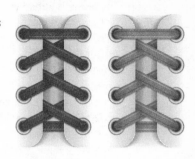
    a. Confide in Fantasia and ask her to defect. > Go to question 23.
    b. Report to HQ that Fantasia is the spy. > MISSION ACCOMPLISHED.
    c. Nothing. You can't betray a friend, even if it means betraying your government. > MISSION FAIL.
22. She is! You pay careful attention, and before long, you can decipher the coded messages she knots into her laces. She is sending messages about circus routines to a rival circus school across town — one funded by the Tribletan government! You send your own message back to HQ via your hair braid. You sadly wave goodbye to Fantasia as she is carted off to spy jail. > MISSION ACCOMPLISHED.
23. Fantasia defects! You . . .
    a. become her BFF, but then she betrays you by blabbing all your secrets to another spy at HQ. > MISSION FAIL. Never trust another spy.
    b. turn her over to HQ. Fantasia turns out to be the best counterspy your nation has ever had. She also turns out to be a terrific dog trainer and helps you stop your dog Ditzy from peeing on the carpet. > MISSION ACCOMPLISHED.

24. The horse is actually two spies in a horse costume, who were spying on you! You capture them and refuse to feed them their oats unless they come with you to HQ. > MISSION ACCOMPLISHED.

25. You discover the horse is being controlled remotely by a horse trainer employed by a rival spy agency. They have fitted out her eyes with contact lenses containing mini (but noisy!) cameras, and her hooves with teeny tiny explosive devices that will make the horse buck when they discharge. The enemy's plan? To throw you off her back during your number and disable you permanently! Once you realize what is going on, you fight back. You trace the wireless messages going from Whinny's eyes and hooves back to a nearby coffee shop. The enemy horse trainer is drinking a latte in a supply cupboard in the back. You immobilize her with horse tranquilizer and let your colleagues cart her off to the glue factory near Gimli, Manitoba. > MISSION ACCOMPLISHED.

Where in the World?

You've just been handed a critical mission assignment
that will take you all over the world. But when you look at
your instructions (coded, of course) you realize there are
no coordinates. Instead, you've been given the vaguest of
details about your destination. Can you find your way to
complete your mission?

1. Prevent the enemy agent, Chris Cross, from crossing the longest
   bridge in the world. Where will you go?
   a. To China, where the Danyang–Kunshan Grand Bridge is
      located.
   b. To the United States, where the Lake Pontchartrain Causeway
      is located.
2. Meet your contact, Sad Eyes, at an internationally known
   landmark that Mughal Emperor Shah Jahan built as a memorial
   for his dead wife. Where will you go?
   a. To Egypt, where the Great Pyramid of Giza is located.
   b. To India, where the Taj Mahal is located.
   c. To Inner Mongolia, where the Zhaojun Tomb is located.
3. Collect a secret document from the heel of a boot concealed in a
   post box in the largest city in the world. Where will you go?
   a. New York (USA).
   b. Tokyo (Japan).
   c. Manila (Philippines).
4. You must prevent a military
   coup! Your only information —
   that it will take place in World
   Heritage Site Machu Picchu,
   next Tuesday. What country
   will you fly to next Monday?
   a. Uruguay.
   b. Paraguay.
   c. Peru.

81

5. It's up to you to save the universe — which you can only do if you safely bungee jump off of Mount Everest without dropping the nuclear device you have wrenched from the maniacal grip of a deranged yeti. If you have to subtract ten metres from the height of the famous mountain to have a safe margin, how long should your bungee cord be?
   a. 8,838 m.
   b. 8,123 m.
   c. 1,823 m.

6. Convince an enemy agent, Hailey Lasso, to become a double agent working for you. The glitch? She only speaks Amharic (and you don't). What country is she most likely from?
   a. Amhara.
   b. Ghana.
   c. Ethiopia.

7. The DEW Line (Distant Early Warning Line) was a system of radar stations set up high in the Arctic during the Cold War to detect incoming Russian bombers. Your mission: to update HQ on whether or not any of the now-crumbling (but still very cool!) installations can be repurposed for the 21st century. What country will you travel to, to find the most installations?
   a. Greenland.
   b. Canada.
   c. Iceland.

8. You must deliver "roses" (psst — they're actually compass roses, drawn on top-secret maps) to your contact. You will connect with her at the southwest corner of the Panama Canal. What body of water will you be beside?
   a. The Pacific Ocean.
   b. The Atlantic Ocean.
   c. The Indian Ocean.

9. Your contact, who hails from Nunavut, has told you she has placed the secret document you need between the stones of an inukshuk. What is an inukshuk?

   a. A kind of house designed especially for the harsh Arctic climate.

   b. A kind of landmark for finding your way across the featureless Arctic landscape.

   c. A rubble field left behind by a retreating glacier.

10. Find Land's End. It sounds like a coded riddle, doesn't it? Your case officer, Agent Sphinx, did give you an additional clue, though. She said, "Have a yummy Cornish pasty for me when you get there!" Where will you go to find Land's End — and a Cornish pasty?

    a. England.

    b. Kansas.

    c. Endland.

SCORING

Give yourself 1 point for each correct answer.

1. a	4. c	7. b	9. b
2. b	5. a	8. a	10. a
3. b	6. c		

HOW YOU RATE . . .

0-3 Where in the world did you go? Your superiors can't find you — to fire you.

4-6 Where in the world is your suitcase? En route to mission success!

7-10 Where in the world is your gold star? On your successful mission completion report, of course!

Do You Dare or Do You Scare?

Spies doing covert actions need to be daring. How daring are you? Find out by choosing your preference from the options below.

1. Would you rather . . .
   a. do an interpretive dance onstage in front of 3,000 annoyed hockey fans (you're delaying the start of the third period), or . . .
   b. eat 100 live worms?

2. Would you rather . . .
   a. BASE jump off the CN Tower, or . . .
   b. get shot out of a cannon at the CrayCray Circus?

3. Would you rather . . .
   a. be responsible for keeping a secret that 500 people's lives depend on, or . . .
   b. blow the whistle and save 500 people, but have your life be imperiled?

4. Would you rather . . .
   a. ride bareback through the desert on a dragon with red-hot skin, or . . .
   b. carry a cold, wet seal across the frozen tundra on your bare back?

5. Would you rather . . .
   a. lick one poison cane toad, or . . .
   b. get licked by 50 poisonous snakes?

6. Would you rather . . .
   a. be interrogated in a cell by your enemies for three days without a chance to sleep, or . . .
   b. be kept in solitary confinement for a week with no food?

7. Would you rather . . .
   a. be cornered by three enemy agents with poison-tipped umbrellas, or . . .
   b. attend a banquet with your great-aunt Lizzie and listen to twenty-four long-winded toasts in a foreign language?
8. Would you rather . . .
   a. eat a raw oyster well past its best-before date, or . . .
   b. eat a live cockroach?
9. Would you rather . . .
   a. squeeze through a tiny space, into a tiny cave — in the dark, or . . .
   b. swim across a river full of hungry, hungry hippos?
10. Would you rather . . .
    a. drive a snowmobile across a four-kilometre-wide frozen lake that is — *CRACK!* — already starting to break up, or . . .
    b. take control of a train that is carrying a bomb that will explode if you don't maintain a speed of exactly 120 km/hr at all times?

SCORING

1. a10 b5	4. a15 b10	7. a20 b5	9. a5 b10
2. a15 b10	5. a10 b20	8. a10 b5	10. a15 b0
3. a0 b20	6. a10 b5		

HOW YOU RATE . . .

55-75 Sensible Serena. You may be too cautious for covert work. But consider yourself lucky — those out-there spykids tend to have very short lifespans. You are the ideal candidate for a comfy, safe analytical job at HQ. (Bonus: they bring in free cupcakes for the staff every Friday!)

80-110 Look-Before-You-Leap Lola. You are an admirable mixture of caution and bravado. You can be relied on to take risks in the field, as long as they do not involve possible death, dismemberment or the need to raid your piggy bank. You can be counted on to make dead drops in boring locations — the most important and common covert operation of all.

115-140 Leap-Before-You-Look Lucy. You are almost the ideal sort of risk taker, with exactly what it takes to be a successful covert agent. You listen to your gut (and your gut always shouts, "DO IT! DO IT! DO IT!"). Luckily you are not a fool, and you won't take a dare where the odds of success are grim. Your next daring act should be — applying for spy school!

145 Wacky Wanda. You are off the charts! You will do almost anything, no matter how crazy. You may wind up saving the universe. But more likely, you'll wind up in emerg with 207 broken bones. Consider a covert career alongside Sensible Serena — in a dull but safe desk job — if you wish to continue having birthdays.

Mission 3 — What Would You Do?

This quiz is designed to simulate a typical mission. Answer the questions to find out how well you might do on your real-life tasks in the field.

1. You find yourself in the ballroom of the Ritz Catton hotel, at a fancy birthday party for your great-aunt Sara, wearing an itchy lace dress and squeaky, too-tight shoes. Your mission is . . .

   a. to get out of these uncomfortable clothes, pronto. > Go to question 2.

   b. to make contact with, and win the trust of, an enemy agent who goes by the name of Bond James Bond. > Go to question 3.

2. You find the nearest washroom and peel off the itchy dress. Underneath you are wearing a black tank and black tights. From your bejewelled purse, you pull out more appropriate shoes — thin, flexible ballet flats. Ready to go, you . . .

   a. stand on the toilet, push up on the ceiling tile and crawl into the hotel ductwork. > Go to question 4.

   b. head to the hotel's lobby. > Go to question 5.

3. You read the brief on Bond James Bond. You discover that Bond James Bond is a fake identity. He is actually an enemy agent named Matilda Earwax, who is extremely adept at disguise! The only way to find Matilda will be through DNA testing of everyone you meet. You . . .

   a. use your incredible A+ science skills and develop a DNA test that can be administered by simply looking at someone. You

get HQ to assign an agent to Heathrow airport, where the entire world eventually passes through. It takes fourteen years, but then — *ta-dah!* The Heathrow agent sends you a picture. And in it Matilda Earwax is checking a pair of skis into oversized luggage. > Go to question 25.

b. Using your incredible computer skills, you create an online game show called *Makeover Magic*. Contestants compete to demonstrate their most incredible makeovers — and disguises. > Go to question 26.

4. You crawl through the ductwork until you find the vent that leads to the outside. You use your handy-dandy electronic screwdriver to remove the vent cover and exit the vent. You find yourself . . .

a. dangling fifteen stories over a canal cutting through the jammed streets of Hong Kong. > Go to question 6.

b. 25 metres from a window in the seedy hotel next door — the window to the room belonging to Bond James Bond. > Go to question 7.

5. A boy who can only be Bond James Bond (he is wearing a name tag that reads, "Hi, my name is Bond James Bond.") approaches you. You encourage him to sit next to you and chat. You . . .

a. ask him where his mother is. He leaves in a huff. > MISSION FAIL.

b. invite him to lunch in the very fancy restaurant on top of the tallest tower in the city. > Go to question 24.

6. You unwrap the spider-steel nano-fibre dental floss you have looped around your pinky toe and tie it to the ductwork. You then . . .

a. step out into the night and, gripping the floss in your teeth, slide fifteen stories down to the canal and the waiting speedboat. > Go to question 8.

b. turn around and return to the hotel washroom, flush the toilet three times and leave the hotel by the front door. > Go to question 9.

7. You toss a line of the spider-steel nano-fibre dental floss that you have hidden in your belly button across the divide, where it sticks like glue. You climb out the window and, hand over hand, cross the gap. When you reach the other side, you smash the window glass and swing into Bond James Bond's hotel suite. Once inside you . . .

   a. discover Bond James Bond eating breakfast. > Go to question 18.

   b. admire the flat-screen TV, then scan the room for clues and secrets. > Go to question 19.

8. As you race off in the speedboat, you hear an enormous explosion. The hotel! It must have been Bond James Bond! You look over your shoulder. He is following you in another speedboat! You . . .

   a. put your pedal to the metal, and your boat goes even faster. But Bond James Bond is still gaining on you! And he's about to leap from his boat right onto yours! > Go to question 16.

   b. put your hands up and mouth the words, "I surrender." > Go to question 17.

9. The toilet flush was your signal to your cohort in conspiracy, Agent 3.14159 (you call her Pia for short). You go to your pre-arranged meeting spot and wait until Agent 3.14159 arrives, somewhat out of breath. You tell her . . .

   a. "The smoke bomb will go off in 3 . . . 2 . . . 1 . . . *BOOOOOF!*" > Go to question 10.

   b. "I spiked Bond James Bond's lemonade with the truth serum you left for me in the third stall." > Go to question 11.

10. With your agency-issued laser vision enhancer, you watch as everyone comes streaming out of the hotel. Bond James Bond is not among them. "Now!" you say. You and Agent Pia . . .

a. don your invisible gas masks and run back into the smoke-filled building, where you find Bond James Bond lying on the floor beside a large potted plant, unconscious! > Go to question 14.

b. don your invisible gas masks and run back into the smoke-filled building, where you find Bond James Bond hacking and coughing and helping a little old lady out of the building. > Go to question 15.

11. You head back to the hotel, where you find Bond James Bond stretched out on a sofa in the lobby, playing video games. You offer to buy him a soft drink. He agrees. In the hotel's restaurant, you . . .

a. ask him subtle-yet-probing questions designed to draw out his secrets. They work. He tells you his life story. It is incredibly dull. > Go to question 12.

b. tell him flat out you're a spy determined to learn his secrets. As you oh-so-cleverly anticipated, he finds your story both unbelievable and highly amusing. Giggling maniacally, he says, "If you really were a spy, you'd be dying to learn . . ." And then he tells you everything. EVERYTHING! Including the fact that there is a plot designed to bring down your government — this very evening! > Go to question 13.

12. You become so bored by Bond James Bond's dullsville stories, you doze off. The next thing you know, you are tied up in a warehouse by the docks, and Bond James Bond is grilling you! > MISSION FAIL.

13. You surreptitiously tap out a coded message with the toe of your specially constructed morse code shoe. Seconds later, you hear the squeal of sirens as your security detail arrives on site. They cart away Bond James Bond, stop the plot and promote you to Head of the Agency. > MISSION ACCOMPLISHED.

14. You immediately administer the antidote to the knock-out gas that Bond James Bond has inhaled. As Bond James Bond comes around, you whisk him out of the hotel lobby to your safe house. While he recovers, you both gain his trust and pump him for information. You and Pia, together, discover all the secrets of the enemy. > MISSION ACCOMPLISHED, and you and Pia wind up as BFFs.

15. You and Pia give Bond James Bond and the little old lady your gas masks and usher them out of the hotel through the back door, where your security detail awaits. You take your prisoners to a deserted warehouse for interrogation. You discover that not only is Bond a double agent working for the good guys, but the little old lady is actually X, the evil mastermind that has been planning to take over the world and turn it into a cheeseball. > MISSION ACCOMPLISHED.

16. Bond James Bond leaps — and misses! He falls into the water and disappears from sight. > MISSION FAIL.

17. You tell your driver to slow down, and the other boat comes up beside yours. You reach out one delicate hand to Bond James Bond, who helps you into his boat. You . . .

   a. give him a karate chop to the neck that disables him. You direct the driver to bring him to a deserted warehouse, where you interrogate him until he cries for his mama and spills all the beans. > MISSION ACCOMPLISHED.

   b. flatter him. He preens like a rooster and asks you if you're hungry — there's a hot dog cart right there! Over lunch, Bond James Bond tells you absolutely everything. You let him blather on, letting your recorder capture every incriminating word. As you finish your hot dog, your security detail arrives. They take Bond James Bond to an incredibly secure prison on the isle of Elba. > MISSION ACCOMPLISHED.

18. You say . . .
    a. "Oh, hi. Sorry. Must have the wrong room." > Go to question 20.
    b. "Would you happen to have an extra croissant? I'm starving." > Go to question 21.

19. In Bond James Bond's hotel room, you find a pen disguised as a lipstick, a phone disguised as a shoe and a notebook containing the keyword for all of the enemy's secret messages. You also find a photo of Bond James Bond with all the top brass of the enemy agency! How could he be so foolish! You . . .
    a. take photos of everything and leave the room exactly as you found it, making sure to scrape away any trace of the spider-steel nano-fibre dental floss. > MISSION ACCOMPLISHED.
    b. sigh, stretch out on the fluffy bed and turn on the flat screen. When he returns, Bond James Bond is stunned to find you in his room. You point out his sloppiness and tell him you are thoroughly disappointed in him. He says, "Sorry, sis. I let you down again." Because your true mission was to train your irritating brother, who has also been recruited (what were they thinking?) by the agency! > MISSION TO BE CONTINUED...

20. Bond James Bond says, "*Au contraire!* You have arrived in the right room heh, heh." You think he is totally creepy and tell him so. He looks hurt. You apologize. He offers you a croissant. You . . .
    a. accept, hoping you can fool him into revealing his secrets over breakfast. > Go to question 22.
    b. decline and disable him with the clownifier gun you cleverly secreted in your earring. > Go to question 23.

21. Bond James Bond invites you to join him for breakfast. You do. He tells you how much he admires a gal who can swing from one building to the next on a strand of spider-steel nano-fibre dental floss. You say how much you admire a guy that has extra croissants. He laughs. He likes you. He invites you to come for a bike ride — he just happens to have two very fast Italian bicycles in the hotel garage! He is awed by you, and winds up telling you everything as you race around the spectacular island on his matching bikes. Sucker. > MISSION ACCOMPLISHED.

22. A few minutes later, you start to feel woozy. He has spiked your chocolate croissant with neurotoxin! And now you are paralyzed and slightly sick to your stomach and he is manoeuvring you to the window about to toss you over! You ...

    a. have a bit of feeling remaining in your right foot. You stamp on his toe with your glass-breaking ballet flat, and he howls in pain. He drops you as he reaches for his foot but oops, falls and accidentally smacks his head against yours, knocking you both out. > MISSION FAIL.

    b. get tossed out of the building! Luckily, your black tank top has secret flying-squirrel wings folded into it, which automatically deploy and allow you to glide to safety. You land on the roof of HQ, where technicians give you the antitoxin and save your life. Bond James Bond is arrested and convicted of attempted murder and sent to jail for life. There, he writes his memoirs and reveals all. > MISSION ACCOMPLISHED.

23. You call HQ, they send a security detail and cart Bond James Bond away. They scold you for turning him into a clown, but they are still happy you captured him without any bloodshed. > MIS-SION SORT-OF ACCOMPLISHED.

24. As long as you smile and nod, he spills secrets! So you pretend to become his bestie, and spend the next year nodding and smiling, nodding and smiling, all the time transmitting key secrets to HQ. > MISSION ACCOMPLISHED.

25. You immediately contact HQ to tell them you have identified and located Bond James Bond, but the phone number has been disconnected. You've been in the field too long and the agency no longer exists! > MISSION FAIL.

26. Before long, Bond James Bond applies to be on your show. You say he must provide you with both a detailed personal history — and his current address — before he can appear on air. He tells all. ALL! > MISSION ACCOMPLISHED.

LOOK FOR THESE OTHER GREAT QUIZ BOOKS!